Usborne

My BIG Magical Colouring Book

Illustrated by Jenny Addison

Words by Kate Nolan

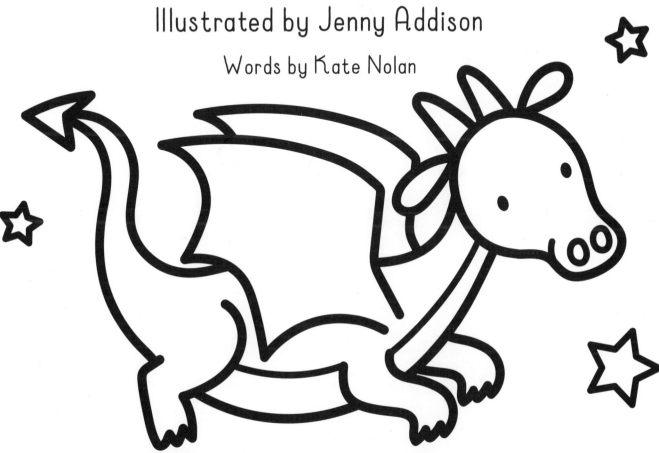

My spells make
everything sparkle!

There's magic
in the air.

Welcome to the world, little dragon.

Fly high like
a phoenix!

A rainbow in
the clouds

Diving below
the waves

Soaring among the stars

This book of spells
belongs to...

...a wise old wizard.

Make a wish!

A fluttering butterfly fairy

Fairy-tale towers
and turrets

How high
can you fly?

Welcome
to the magic
garden!

Enchanted
toadstools

Hello, happy unicorn.

Ready for a trip to Fairyland!

My basket is full
of pretty blossoms.

Spring flowers dancing
in the breeze

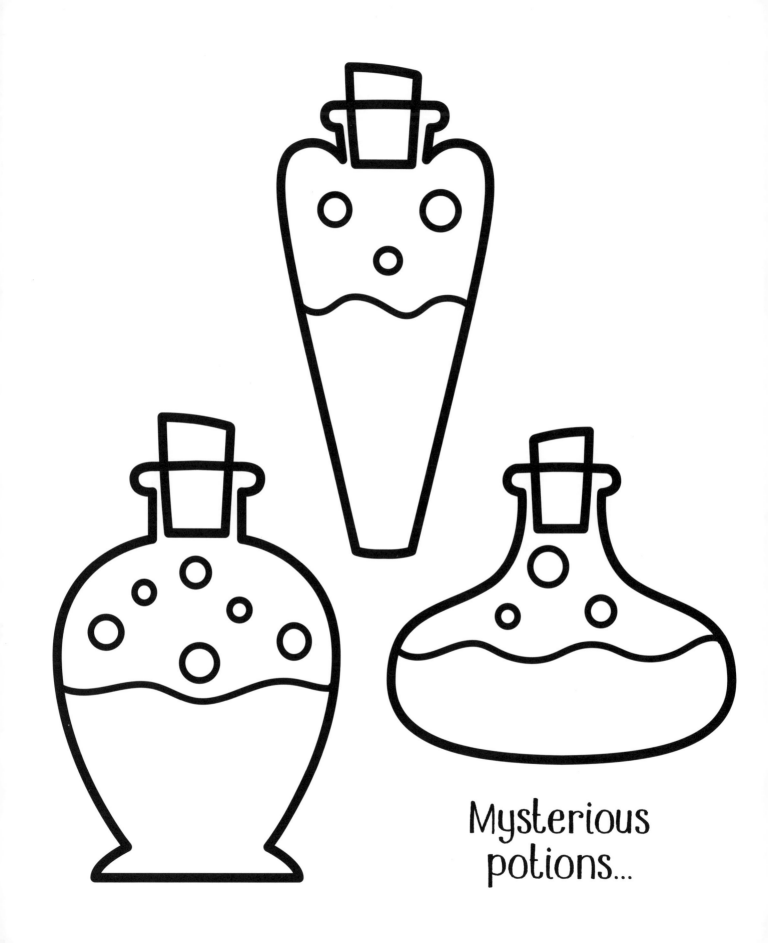

Mysterious
potions...

It's the most
magical time
of the year.

I'm casting my
sparkliest spell.

A mermaid
flicking her tail

A unicorn
seahorse
swimming
along

A sprinkling of fairy
dust will do the trick.

Come on,
narwhal,
let's race!

A dragon
with fiery
breath

Croak crrrroak!

A witch's cottage in the moonlight

Full moon and
twinkling stars

Whizzing through the snow

Where will you go next?

A fairy with her
butterfly friend

I'm guarding a
spooky castle!

A friendly dragon

A castle deep in the sea

I love looking in
my magic mirror!

Bye-bye,
butterfly!

I wonder who
lives here?

A hooting owl

A crumpled
witch's hat

Snow is
falling at the
fairy palace.

Brrr... wrap up warm!

On summer days,
butterflies flutter...

...and fairies play.

Busy elves are making toys...

...in Santa's magical workshop.

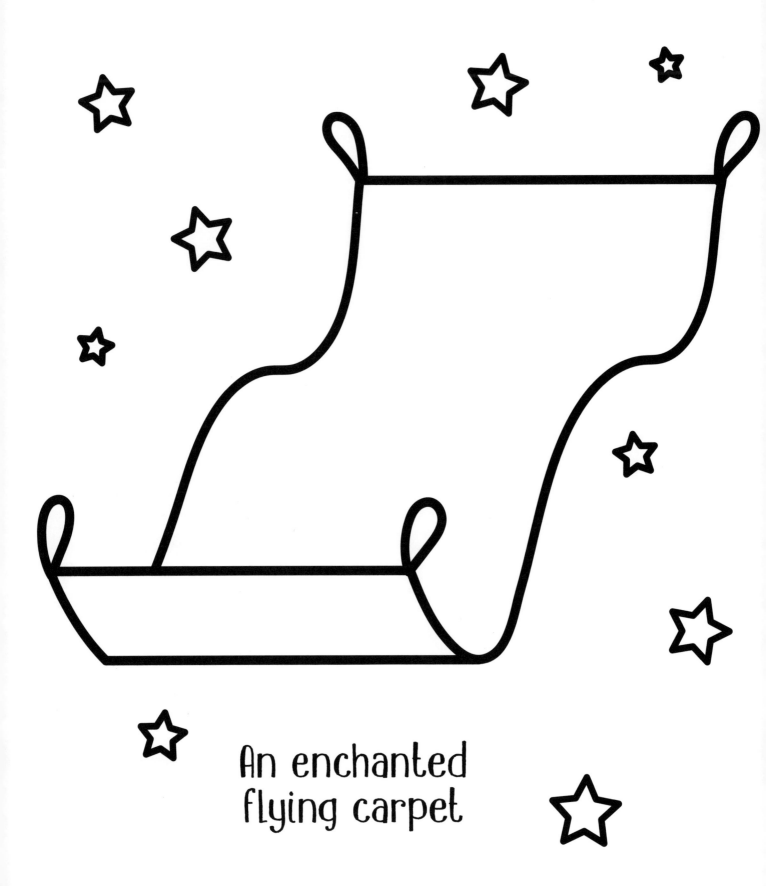

An enchanted
flying carpet

What will
you wish for?

Good morning,
Sea King!

Can I play
you a song?

Look what
I've caught!

A fairy
fast asleep

Swooping through
the starry sky

Snowstorms
are the
BEST!

Watch out for
the monster
plant!

I've picked lots of juicy apples.

Meow! I'm a witch's cat.

Getting
ready to fly

Shhh... it's nap time for unicorns!

Visiting a castle
in the clouds

A jolly
elf with a
pointed hat

I think spring
is here!

I love sitting on a toadstool.

Pixie boots
with pompoms

My garden is growing nicely.

Hello,
seahorse,
how are you?

It's a wonderful
day for flying!

A yummy cupcake

Hi there, troll!

These magic
crystals are
SO shiny.

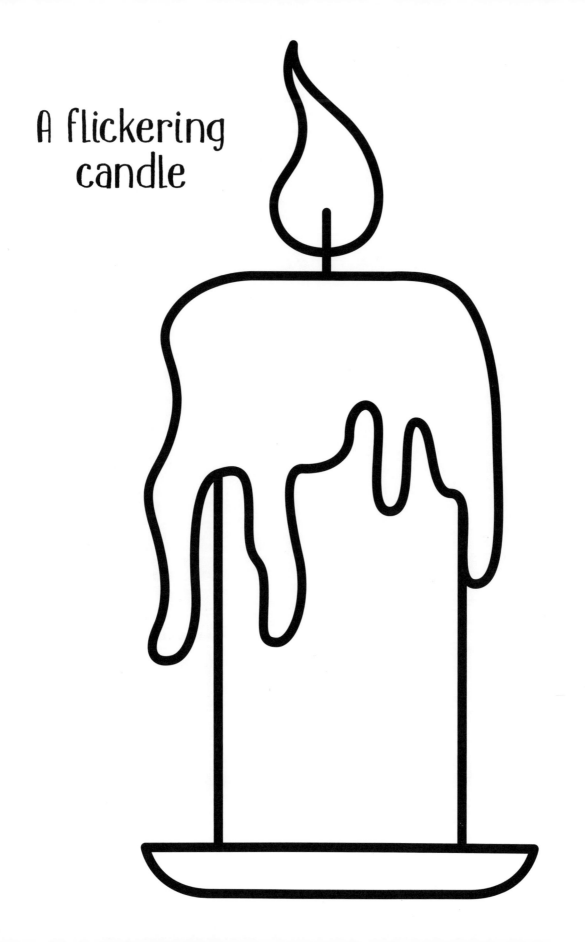

A flickering candle

Flitting
through the
night sky

A mermaid
princess

Abracadabra!

A magic
beanstalk
to climb

A smiling centaur

Yum... this unicorn
cake looks delicious!

Galloping
through the fields

An elf's house in the treetops

Splash! It's
nice and dry
under here.

Spread your
wings and FLY!

Dragon eggs
ready to
hatch

Let's explore
the enchanted
caves!

This ring
has magic
powers...

It's nice to
see you, crab!

A swirly, whirly sea dragon

A shimmering crystal ball

A wizard's
hat covered
in stars

It's fun to play among the flowers.

Back home after a magical day

Night-night,
dragon. Sweet
dreams!